C000155765

50 Great Irish Love Songs

Compiled by

Robert Gogan

© 2002 by Robert Gogan, 61 Grosvenor Square, Rathmines, Dublin 6, Ireland
All rights reserved. Worldwide copyright secured.

Published by Music Ireland, 61 Grosvenor Square, Rathmines, Dublin 6, Ireland
Web page: http://www.music-ireland.ie

"I Know My Love", "I Know Where I'm Going" and "Danny Boy" (The Derry Air) reproduced by kind permission of Boosey & Hawkes Music Publishers Limited.
"Danny Boy" - Trad/Frederick E. Weatherly/Harold Samuel**:** © 1913 by Boosey & Company Limited
"I Know My Love" – Trad/Herbert Hughes: © 1909 by Boosey & Company Limited
"I Know Where I'm Going"- Trad/Herbert Hughes**:** © 1909 by Boosey & Company Limited

Every effort has been made to ascertain the ownership of, and rights over, each song.   Any infringement of existing rights over any song or part of a song is unintentional and the publisher requests that he be notified immediately of any such infringement.

"The Golden Jubilee": copyright control
"The Sally Gardens": copyright control

Photocopying this work is illegal under the Copyright Acts

Printed by: Mount Salus Press, Dublin
Designed and complied by: Robert Gogan
Book cover design: Ed McGinley, MGA Design Consultants, Dublin

Front cover photographs courtesy of Bord Fáilte – The Irish Tourist Board
"Girl with sunlit hair" by Brian Lynch
"Sunset, Rossnowlagh, County Donegal" by Pat O'Dea

CD
Recorded at Sonic Studios, Dublin.
Engineer: Al Cowan
Produced by Robert Gogan

Musicians
Sinéad Martin (Guitar/Vocals)
Tracks 2, 6, 7, 9, 12, 14, 16, 22, 28, 29, 33, 40, 41, 45.
John Doyle (Vocals) / Roddy Gallagher (Guitar)
Tracks 1, 3, 4, 5, 8, 10, 11, 13, 15, 17, 18, 19, 20, 21, 23, 24, 25, 26, 27, 30, 31, 32, 34, 35, 36, 37, 38, 39, 42, 43, 44, 46.
Robert Gogan (Guitar/Vocals)
Tracks: 47, 48, 49, 50.

ISBN 0 9532068 1 5

50 GREAT IRISH LOVE SONGS

INTRODUCTION

The Irish make great lovers, and these songs prove it!
In this book you have all you need to learn to play and sing some of the greatest Irish love songs ever written – the lyrics, guitar chords and simplified music score.
And what a magnificent selection of songs, from the haunting "Danny Boy" and "She Moved Through The Fair" to the beautiful "Mountains Of Mourne" and "Rose Of Tralee" and to the mischievous "German Clockwinder" and "Maids When You're Young" They're all here!
So enjoy these songs! Sing them! Change the words or music or timing if you feel something else works better for you! After all, that's what ballads are all about!

The Chorus

If a song has a chorus it is printed in bold italics *like this*. Some songs start with a chorus and therefore it will be in the main body of the score. Others have the chorus after the first verse.
Choruses are great things – they are a law unto themselves. You can add more in (and this normally depends on the number of verses of the song the singer knows!) or take them out if you want to shorten the song. So do your own thing! Do it your way!
But above all, enjoy these songs! They are crying out to be sung!

I am indebted to the following publications and websites for facts, information and references:

"The Poolbeg Book of Irish Ballads" by Sean McMahon. Poolbeg Press
"The Complete Guide to Celtic Music" by June Skinner Sawyers. Aurum Press
"Bird Life in Ireland" by Don Conroy & Jim Wilson. The O'Brien Press
"The Oxford Companion to Irish History" edited by S.J. Connolly. Oxford University Press
"AA Illustrated Road Book of Ireland" The Automobile Association
"Irish Ballads" edited by Fleur Robertson. Gill & MacMillan

www.contemplator.com/folk
www.standingstones.com
www.mudcat.org
www.geocities.com/shantysong

Robert Gogan

Index By First Line

Guitar chords used in this book

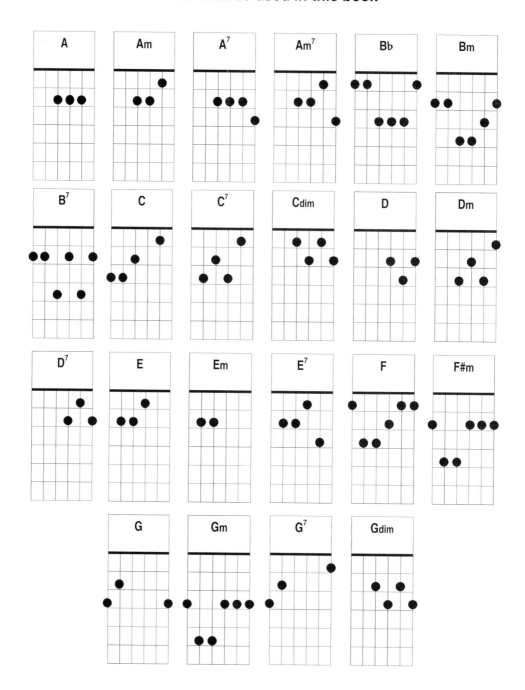

My Singing Bird

The lark (or to use its official name 'Skylark', or *alauda arvensis*) is a very common bird in Ireland. It is estimated that over one million skylarks breed in Ireland each year. Their favourite habitats are the open country and coastal dunes. They make their nests on the ground, usually under clumps of tall grass. It often perches and sings on fence posts. One of the great characteristics of the skylark is their practice of flying at high altitude, especially over stubble fields where they find most of their food – cereal grain and insects. It's one of the first birds to be heard in the morning in open countryside – hence they have earned the reputation as a kind of symbol of the morning and the dawn of a new day. Its continuous song consists of a constant jumble of twittering, chirping and warbling sounds, often including the imitation of other song birds. It sings as it ascends into the heavens and hovers on fluttering wings, sometimes until it is almost out of sight.

If you want to keep your eyes open to spot skylarks their main features are sandy brown upper parts, streaked with dark brown. They have white outer tail feathers with a thin white trailing edge to their wings, visible only when open. Their underside consists of a white belly, buff breast with dark streaking, heaviest on the sides. Their bills are pale, short and stubby. They have long legs, pale pink in colour with a very long claw on the hind toe.

If disturbed on the ground they will usually flutter off a short distance and land in the long grass. There is another song in this book relating to the skylark – see The Lark in the Morning (page 46).

If I could lure my singing bird down from its own cosy nest
If I could catch my singing bird I'd warm it upon my breast
And in my heart my singing bird would sing itself to rest
Ah, etc. would sing itself to rest

The Mountains Of Mourne

This is one of Percy French's (1854 – 1920) most famous songs. He is reputed to have written it in 1896 on a very clear day, when he could see the Mountains of Mourne from the Hill of Howth in North Dublin.

William Percy French was born on May 1st 1854 in Cloonyquin, Co. Roscommon – in the mid-west of Ireland. He was reared in affluent circumstances and educated at upmarket English schools and at Trinity College, Dublin. He certainly could not be described as a 'model student' at Trinity College, for he established the record during his 'studies' for the student who took the longest time to obtain a degree!

While most of French's songs are humorous and entertaining, they never ridicule, but show a warm and genuine love of the Irish country folk about whom he wrote. This song is about a lonely Irish emigrant working in London and writing a letter to his beloved in Ireland.

Apart from writing many well-remembered and popular 'drawing-room' songs he was also a fine landscape painter. Today, many of his watercolours command high prices at art auctions.

The Mountains of Mourne are situated in County Down, in the north-east of Ireland. This mountain range, the highest in Northern Ireland, is dominated by Slieve Donard, at 2,796 feet. In clear weather, the Welsh and English Lake District mountains can be seen, as well as the Isle of Arran and the Isle of Man.

I believe that when writing a wish you expressed; As to how the young ladies of London were dressed
Well, if you'll believe me, when asked to a ball; Sure they don't wear a top to their dresses at all
Oh I've seen them myself and you could not in truth; Say if they were bound for a ball or a bath
Don't be starting them fashions now, Mary mo chroí*; Where the Mountains of Mourne sweep down to the sea.

I've seen England's King from the top of a bus; Sure I never knew him but he means to know us
And though by the Saxon we once were oppressed; Still I cheered, God forgive me, I cheered with the rest
And now that he's visited Erin's green shore; We'll be much better friends than we've been heretofore
When we've got all we want we're as quiet as can be; Where the Mountains of Mourne sweep down to the sea

You remember young Peter O'Loughlin, of course; Well now he is here at the head of the Force
I met him today; I was crossing the Strand; And he stopped the whole street with one wave of his hand
And as we stood talking of days that were gone; The whole population of London looked on
But for all his great powers he's wishful like me; To be back where the dark Mourne sweeps down to the sea

There's beautiful girls here; oh never you mind; With beautiful shapes Nature never designed
And lovely complexions; all roses and cream; But O'Loughlin remarked with regard to the same
That if at those roses you venture to sip; The colour might all come away on your lip
So I'll wait for the wild rose that's waiting for me; Where the Mountains of Mourne sweep down to the sea

*Pronounced "cree" (my beloved)

~~~~~~~~~~~~~~

I Know Where I'm Going

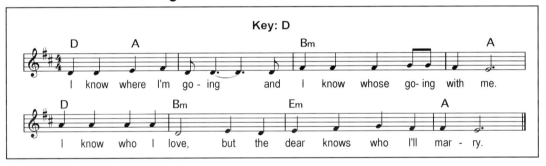

Some will say he's dark, some will say he's bonny
But the fairest of them all is my handsome noble Johnny

I have stockings of silk, shoes of fine green leather
Combs to bind my hair and a ring for every finger

Feather beds are soft and painted rooms are bonny
But I would leave them all to be with my darling Johnny

(Repeat first verse)

3

She Moved Through The Fair

Although I have attributed a 4/4 timing to this song, it doesn't really adhere to a strict tempo. It is a very well know, and beautifully haunting love song.

Without doubt, it's one of my favourite ballads in this collection. I always felt that there was something missing from the storyline of the original version of this ballad which I learned, so I added a verse of my own which I use when I sing this song - just to get across the message that the girl had died or been killed, because that's the impression you get from the last verse of the song.

It was sung by Sinéad O'Connor to great effect in the film "Michael Collins". There is also a lovely version of it by the Breton harpist, Alan Stivell, on his album "Chemin de Terre"

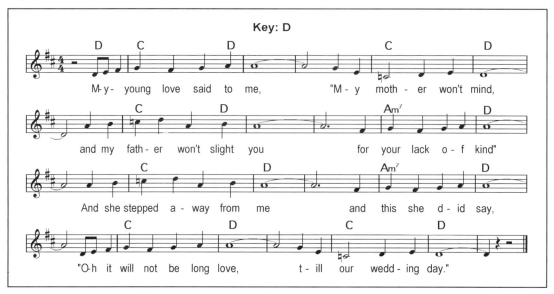

She went away from me and she moved through the fair
And fondly I watched her move here and move there
And she made her way homeward with one star awake
As the swan in the evening moves over the lake

'Twas the last time I saw her when she moved through the fair
And I gazed as the sunlight did dance through her hair
But the wind in the rushes their secret do keep
Like the waves on the shoreline, that my love's asleep

Last night I did dream that my love she came in
And so softly she came that her feet made no din
And she laid her hand on me and smiling did say
"It will not be long love, till our wedding day"

The Hills Of Kerry

(Verses and chorus have the same melody)

The pa-lm trees wave on high, all a-long the fer-tile shore.
A-dieu the hills of Ke-rr-y I'll ne'-er see you no more.
Why did I leave my home. Why did I cross the sea
and leave the small birds si-ng-ing a-rou-nd you sweet Tra-lee.

The noble and the brave have departed from our shore
They've gone off to a foreign land where the mighty canyons roar
No more will they see the shamrock or the hills so dear to me
Or hear the small birds singing all around you, sweet Tralee.
Chorus

No more the sun will shine on that blessed harvest morn
Or hear the reaper singing in the fields of golden corn
There's a balm for every woe and a cure for every pain
But the pretty smile of my darling girl I will never see again.
Chorus

The Rose Of Tralee

This song, now enjoying the status as the County Anthem for County Kerry, was written by William Pembroke Mulchinock (1820 – 1864).

The Mulchinocks were a fairly prosperous family living in Tralee and William fell in love with Mary O'Connor, the daughter of one of the family's servants. His parents were not at all happy with this liaison and young William was quickly despatched abroad for fear that his affections might grow even stronger. Following a spell in France and India William returned to Tralee. Tradition has it that on his arrival back to Tralee he saw a funeral party coming down the street. On making enquiries he was told that the deceased was his beloved Mary O'Connor, who had died from the disease of consumption. William wrote this ballad in her memory, using a local tune about the nearby Ballymullan Castle as his model.

William Mulchinock wrote many poems for various Irish journals, including The Nation newspaper. He left for New York in 1849 and achieved considerable success as a writer of lyrics. In 1851 he published a collection, entitled "The Ballads and Songs of W.P. Mulchinock", which oddly enough, doesn't contain The Rose of Tralee.

He returned to Tralee in 1855 and died there in 1864.

The Rose of Tralee is now one of the best known and loved of all Irish ballads, both at home and abroad. Its popularity and endurance was assisted in no small way by a fine recording of the song made by the Irish tenor, John McCormack, many years ago.

The Capital of County Kerry, Tralee is situated near the mouth of Tralee Bay in the south-west of Ireland and is about 20 miles from Killarney. Tralee is home to a major annual festival which takes place in August, known as the 'Rose of Tralee' Festival, which celebrates the beauty of the Irish Colleen. Tralee also has a fine racecourse and the Tralee Racing Festival held annually at the end of August and well worth a visit!

The cool shades of evening their mantles were spreading
And Mary, all smiling, sat list'ning to me
The moon through the valley her pale rays was shedding
When I won the heart of the Rose of Tralee.
Chorus

The Curragh Of Kildare

This ballad is reputed to be about a Scottish girl who is heartbroken for her beloved who is a British soldier based in the Curragh military camp in Co. Kildare. She is so sorrowful she contemplates disguising herself and enlisting in the army so that she could be with him.

The Curragh is a undulating unenclosed plain of about 5,000 acres which lies immediately east of Kildare town, about 30 miles south-east of Dublin. It derives its name from the Irish word 'An Currach' which means 'The Racecourse'. The magnificent racecourse at The Curragh is the venue for many race meetings, including the Irish Derby.

The Curragh military camp has been in existence for centuries and the British administration established a permanent military base there in 1854. A section of the Irish army is now based there.

Though technically British property in the nineteenth century, an Act of Parliament in 1870 recognised the continuing right of local farmers to graze sheep on The Curragh.

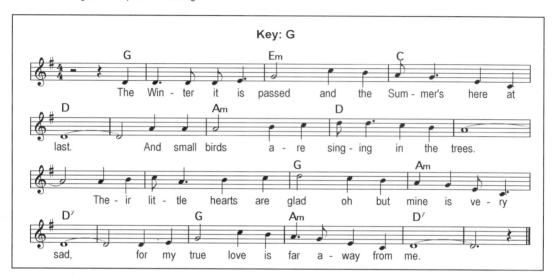

All you that are in love and cannot it remove
I pity all the pain that you endure
For experience lets me know that your hearts are full of woe
It's a woe that no mortal can endure

A livery I will wear and I'll straighten back my hair
In velvet so green I will appear
And it's then I will repair to the Curragh of Kildare
For it's there I'll find tidings of my dear

The rose upon the briar and the water running free
Gives joy to the linnet and the bee
Their little hearts are blessed but mine is not at rest
For my true love is absent from me

*And it's then I will repair to the Curragh of Kildare
For it's there I'll find tidings of my dear

*Sung to the melody of the last two lines

8

The Bonny Boy

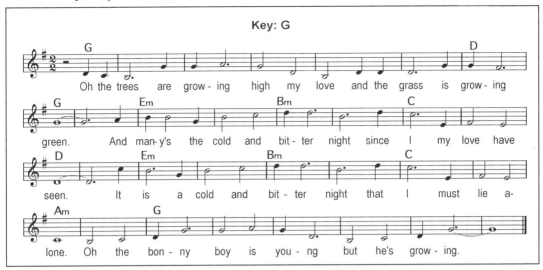

Key: G

Oh the trees are grow-ing high my love and the grass is grow-ing green. And man-y's the cold and bit-ter night since I my love have seen. It is a cold and bit-ter night that I must lie a-lone. Oh the bon-ny boy is you-ng but he's grow-ing.

Oh Father dear father I think you did me wrong
For to go and get me married to one who is so young
For he is only sixteen years and I am twenty-one
And the bonny boy is young and still growing

Oh daughter dear daughter I did not do you wrong
For to go and get you married to one who is so young
I'm sure he'll be a match for you when I am dead and gone
Oh the bonny boy is young but he's growing

Oh Father dear father I'll tell you what I'll do
I'll send my love to college for another year or two
And all around his college cap I'll tie a ribbon blue
Just to show the other girls that he's married

At evening when strolling down by the college wall
You'd see the young collegiates a-playing at the ball
You'd see him in amongst them there, the fairest of them all
He's my bonny boy, he's young but he's growing

At the early age of sixteen years he was a married man
And at the age of seventeen the father of a son
But at the age of eighteen o'er his grave the grass grew strong
Cruel death put an end to his growing

I will make my love a shroud of the highest Holland brown
And whilst I am a-weaving it my tears they will flow down
For once I had a true love but now he's lying low
And I'll nurse his bonny boy while he's growing

9

Red Is The Rose

(Verses and chorus have the same melody)

This is a simple and charming Irish ballad sung to the air of the Scottish tune "Loch Lomond".

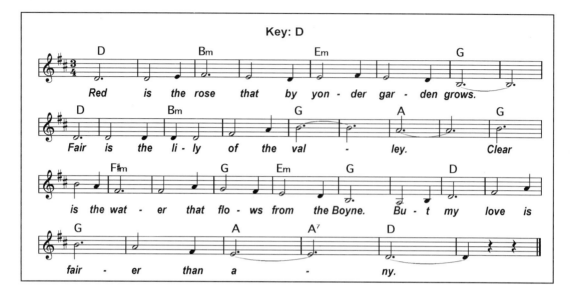

'Twas down by Killarney's green woodlands that we strayed
The moon and the stars they were shining
The moon shone its rays on her locks of golden hair
She swore she'd be my love forever
Chorus

But time passes on and my darling girl is gone
She's gone and she's met with another
I'm full of regret but my heart will ne'er forget
That once she was truly my lover
Chorus

It's not for the parting that my sister pains
It's not for the grief of my mother
It's all for the loss of my bonnie Irish lass
That my heart is breaking forever
Chorus

A Bunch Of Thyme

"Thyme" in this ballad is a reference to innocence and virginity and the ballad suggests that you should never trust a sailor!

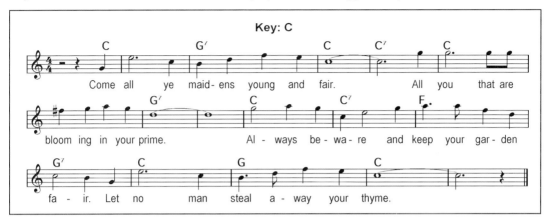

For thyme, it is a precious thing
And thyme brings all things to my mind
Thyme with all its flavours, along with all its joys
Thyme brings all things to my mind

Once I had a bunch of thyme
I thought it never would decay
Then came a lusty sailor who chanced to pass my way
He stole my bunch of thyme away

The sailor gave to me a rose
A rose that never would decay
He gave it to me, to keep me reminded
Of when he stole my thyme away

(Repeat first verse)

The Last Rose Of Summer

This ballad was written by Thomas Moore (1779 – 1852) who is renowned as one of Ireland's greatest songwriters. He was a student in Trinity College, Dublin and was also a friend of Robert Emmet, the Irish patriot who led a small and abortive insurrection in Dublin in 1803 and was executed for his efforts. He was also acquainted with many of the United Irishmen and contributed to their newspaper, "The Press".

Combining his compositions with famous Irish airs of the period, he published his works in the famous collections known as "Irish Melodies", but now more popularly known as "Moore's Irish Melodies" or "Moore's Melodies". There were ten volumes, the first appearing in 1807 and the final one (with a supplement) appearing in 1834. The "Irish Melodies" were immensely popular in Ireland and Britain.

Moore, in his "Irish Melodies" was seeking a rich and sophisticated audience for his songs and the first volume was dedicated to "the Nobility and Gentry of Ireland". Moore was attempting to portray a more peaceful side to Irish Nationalism and his ballads are a far cry from the blood-thirsty and rebel-rousing ballads which proliferated the streets and ale houses in the early nineteenth century.

There were two distinctly different attitudes among Irishmen towards Moore's ballads. Many though that he had achieved more to awaken the nationalistic spirit of Irishmen than the rebel-rousing ballads more familiar to the Irish ear, while others regarded them as whinging songs, bemoaning our downtrodden state and hanging from the coat-tails of the oppressor pleading for mercy. Some of Moore's ballads were reprinted on street ballad broadsheets throughout the middle years of the nineteenth century, particularly such songs as "Let Erin Remember", and the popular "The Minstrel Boy".

The ballads of Thomas Moore reproduced in this book do not reflect on the patriotic side of his writings, but more on the romantic - see "Believe Me, If All Those Endearing Young Charms" (page 20) and "The Meeting Of The Waters" (page 34).

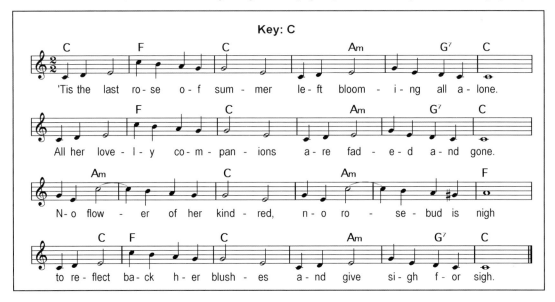

I'll not leave thee, thou alone one, to pine on the stem
Since the lovely are sleeping go sleep, thou, with them
Thus kindly I scatter thy leaves o'er the bed
Where thy mates of the garden lie scentless and dead

So soon may I follow when friendships decay
And from love's shining circle the gems drop away
When true hearts lie withered and fond ones are flown
Oh who would inhabit this bleak world alone!

When You Were Sweet Sixteen

This popular love song was made even more so by a recording of it by the Irish folk group The Furey Brothers in the 1970's.

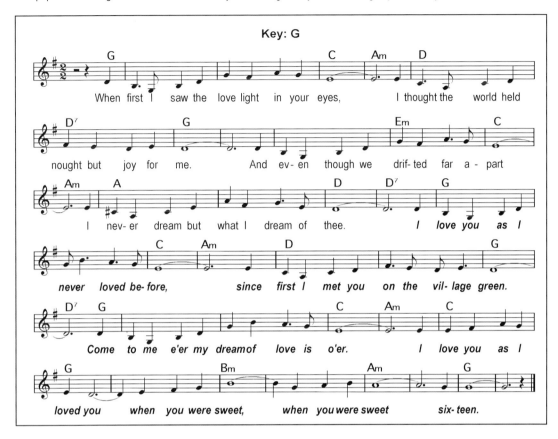

Last night I dreamt I held your hand in mine
And once again you were my happy bride
I kissed you as I did in 'Auld Lang Syne'
As to the church we wandered side by side
Chorus

Bunclody

Bunclody is a town situated in County Wexford, on Ireland's east coast – about 76 miles from Dublin. At Bunclody the River Slaney is joined with the River Clody. To the south-west rises Mount Leinster (2610 feet). The town was formerly known as Newtownbarry in recognition of its patron, James Barry, Sovereign of Naas, whose daughter Judith married one John Maxwell, who was granted a patent for Fairs at Bunclody in 1720. In 1798 insurgents under Father Kearns attacked Bunclody in an unsuccessful attempt to open communications with their comrades in Carlow and Wicklow during the 1798 Rebellion.

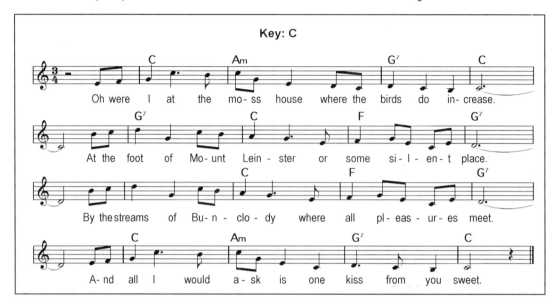

The streams of Bunclody they flow down so free
By the streams of Bunclody I'm longing to be
A-drinking strong liquor in the height of my cheer
Here's a health to Bunclody and the lass I love dear

Oh, 'tis why my love slights me as you might understand
For she has a freehold and I have no land
She has great stores of riches and a fine sum of gold
And everything fitting a house to uphold

If I were a clerk and could write a good hand
I would write my love a letter that she would understand
For I am a young fellow that is wounded in love
Once I lived in Bunclody but now I must remove

So fare thee well father and mother, adieu
My sisters and brothers farewell unto you
I am bound for Americay my fortune to try
When I think of Bunclody I'm ready to die

I'll Tell Me Ma

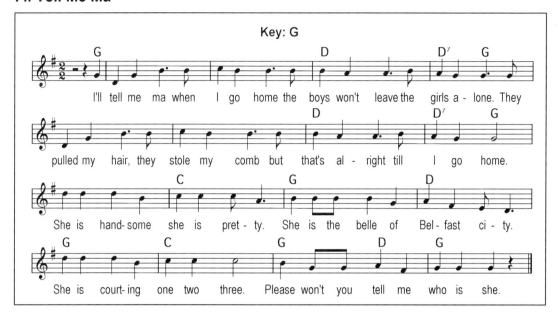

Albert Mooney says he loves her
All the boys are fighting for her
They rap at the door and they ring at the bell
Saying "O my true love are you well"
Out she comes as white as snow
Rings on her fingers bells on her toes
Jenny Murray says she'll die
If she doesn't get the fella with the roving eye

Let the wind and the rain and the hail blow high
And the snow come tumbling from the sky
She's as nice as apple pie
And she'll get her own lad by and by
When she gets a lad of her own
She won't tell her ma when she goes home
But let them all come as they will
It's Albert Mooney she loves still

(Repeat first verse)

Peggy Gordon

I understand that this ballad originated in Scotland. However, it's a well known ballad in Ireland and will be heard at all decent ballad sessions!

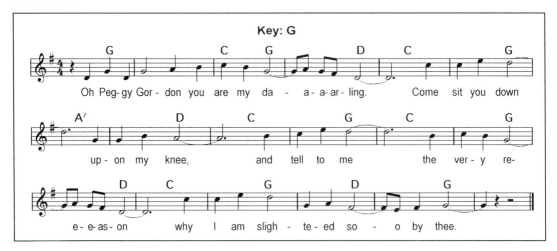

I'm so in love and I can't deny it
My heart is smothered in my breast
It's not for you to let the world know it
A troubled mind sure it knows no rest

I put my head to a glass of brandy
It is my fancy I do declare
For when I'm drinking I'm always thinking
And wishing Peggy Gordon was here

I wish I was in some lonesome valley
Where womankind could not be found
Where little birds sing in the branches
And every moment a different sound

(Repeat the first verse)
(Note that four of the 'C' chords should by played slightly before the relevant note – as per the score)

Love Is Teasing

Marianne Faithful sings a lovely version of this ballad on The Chieftain's album "The Long Black Veil".

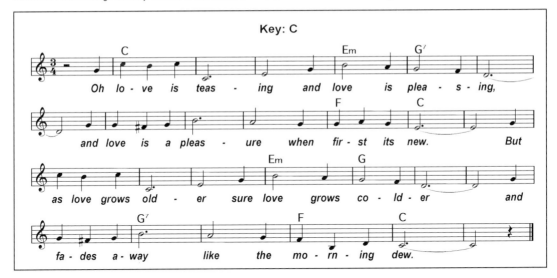

I left my father, I left my mother
I left all my sisters and brothers too
I left all my friends and my own relations
I left them all for to follow you
Chorus

And love and porter make a young man older;
And love and whiskey make an old man grey
What cannot be cured, love, must be endured, love
And now I am bound for Americay
Chorus

The sweetest apple is soonest rotten
The hottest love is the soonest cold
What cannot be cured, love, must be endured, love
And now I am bound for Americay
Chorus

I wish, I wish, I wish in vain
I wish that I was a maid again
But a maid again I can never be
Till apples grow on an ivy tree
Chorus

The Banks Of The Roses

This ballad dates from the end of the 18th century and is thought to have originated in County Limerick.

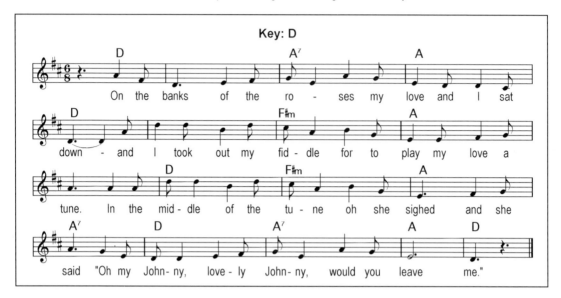

"When I was just a young girl I heard my father say
'I'd sooner see you dead, my girl, and buried in the clay
Rather than be married to a roving runaway
On the lovely sweet banks of the roses' "

Oh well now I am a runaway and sure I'll let you know
That I can take a bottle and drink with anyone
If her father doesn't like me he can keep his daughter home
Then young Johnny will go roving with another

If I ever get wedded 'twill be in the month of May
When the leaves they are green and the meadows they are gay
And me and my true love will sit and sport and play
By the lovely sweet banks of the roses

The Leaving Of Liverpool

This is an English emigration ballad which is very popular in Ireland.

I am sailing upon a Yankee sailing ship
Davy Crockett is her name
And her captain's name is Burgess
And they say she is a floating shame
Chorus

Oh the sun is on the harbour love
And I wish I could remain
For I know it will be a long long time
E'er I see you once again
Chorus

Believe Me, If All Those Endearing Young Charms

This ballad was written in 1808 by Thomas Moore (1779 – 1852) who is considered one of Ireland's greatest songwriters. It is believed that Moore wrote this ballad for his wife who had suffered facial scars due to an attack of smallpox.

The lyrics, written by Moore, were set to an Irish air from the early 1800's. This air was also used for a ballad entitled "My Lodging it is in the Cold Ground"

Thomas Moore was the son of a shoemaker and was born in Dublin on May 28th, 1779. He was a student in Trinity College, Dublin and was also a friend of Robert Emmet, the Irish patriot who led a small and abortive insurrection in Dublin in 1803 and was executed for his efforts. He was also acquainted with many of the United Irishmen and contributed to their newspaper, "The Press".

Combining his composition with famous Irish airs of the period, he published his works in the famous collections known as "Irish Melodies", but now more popularly known as "Moore's Irish Melodies" or "Moore's Melodies". There were ten volumes, the first appearing in 1807 and the final one (with a supplement) appearing in 1834. The "Irish Melodies" were immensely popular in Ireland and Britain. The ten volumes contained 130 poems set to music, mostly old Irish airs.

Moore, in his "Irish Melodies" was seeking a rich and sophisticated audience and the first volume was dedicated to "the Nobility and Gentry of Ireland". Moore was attempting to portray a more peaceful side to Irish Nationalism and his ballads are a far cry from the blood-thirsty and rebel-rousing ballads which proliferated the streets and ale houses in the early nineteenth century.

There were two distinctly different attitudes among Irishmen towards Moore's ballads. Many though that he had achieved more to awaken the nationalistic spirit of Irishmen than the rebel-rousing ballads more familiar to the Irish ear, while others regarded them as whinging songs, bemoaning our downtrodden state and hanging from the coat-tails of the oppressor pleading for mercy. Some of Moore's ballads were reprinted on street ballad broadsheets throughout the middle years of the nineteenth century, particularly such songs as "Let Erin Remember", and the popular "The Minstrel Boy"

The ballads of Thomas Moore reproduced in this book do not reflect on the patriotic side of his writings, but more on the romantic - see "The Last Rose of Summer" (see page 12), "The Meeting Of The Waters" (see page 34).

It is not while beauty and truth are thine own
And thy cheeks unprofaned by a tear
That the fervour and faith of a soul can be known
To which time will but make thee more dear
No, the heart that has truly loved never forgets
But as truly loves on to the close
As the sun-flower turns on her God when he sets
The same look which she turned when he rose

Easy And Slow

'Twas down by Christ-church that I first met with Ann-ie. A neat lit-tle gi-rl and not a bit shy. She told me her fa-ther who came from Dun-gan-non would take her back home in the sweet bye and bye. And what's it to an-y-man wheth-er or no. Wheth-er I'm ea-sy or wheth-er I'm true. As she lift-ed her pett-i-coat ea-sy and slow, And I rolled up my sleeves for to buck-le her shoe.

All along Thomas Street, down to the Liffey; the sunshine was gone and the evening grew dark
Along by Kingsbridge and begod in a jiffy; me arms were around her beyond in the Park
Chorus

From city or county the girl she's a jewel; and well made for gripping the most of them are
But any young man he is really a fool; if he tries at the first time to go a bit far
Chorus

Now if you should go to the town of Dungannon; you can search till your eyes they are weary or blind
Be you lying or walking or sitting or running; a lassie like Annie you never will find
Chorus

The Sally Gardens

This is a beautiful Irish love song, the lyrics of which were written by the poet William Butler Yeats (1865 – 1939).
Yeats is regarded as one of the greatest of the Anglo-Irish poets. His mother's family were merchants from County Sligo – hence his many associations with the county. He spent his formative years in London, Dublin and Sligo.
His first works were published in the 1880's and his poetry drew extensively from Gaelic literature and Sligo folklore. Yeats mobilised the nationalist literary groups at the time into the foundation for a national artistic revival. This culminated in the foundation of the Irish Literary Theatre, later to be called the Abbey Theatre, situated in Dublin.
Yeats won the Nobel Prize for Literature in 1923. He served in the Irish Free State as a Senator from 1922 to 1928.
He died in France in 1939 and in 1948 his remains were re-interred in the quiet graveyard in Drumcliffe, County Sligo. The epitaph on his tombstone ("Cast a cold Eye on Life, on Death. Horseman pass by!") has been the subject of many's a lengthy discussion among Irish literary scholars down through the years.
When Yeats was in the town of Ballisodare in County Sligo he heard a local man singing a plaintive folk tune and this inspired him to write this poem. There was once a row of thatched cottages near the mills at Ballisodare and each of them had a sally garden attached. Yeats considered this to be an ideal place for lovers to meet – hence the song.
Sally (or Salley) comes from the Irish word for willow. Willow rods were used in basket-making and for providing scallops for thatching. They were grown specially for those purposes.
County Sligo is situated on the north-east coast of Ireland. County Sligo, and parts of adjoining County Leitrim, are widely referred to as 'the Yeats Country'.

In a field down by the river
My love and I did stand
And on my leaning shoulder
She laid her snow-white hand
She bid me take life easy
As the grass grows on the weirs
But I was young and foolish
And now am full of tears

(Repeat first verse)

I Never Will Marry

(Verses and chorus have the same melody)

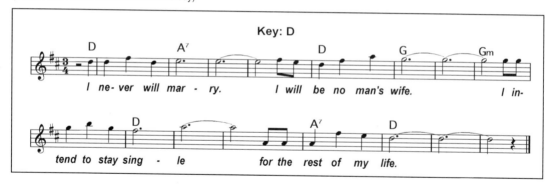

One day as I rambled down by the seashore
The wind it did whistle and the waters did roar
I heard a young maiden make a pitiful cry
She sounded so lonesome at the waters nearby
Chorus

"The shells in the ocean will be my death bed
May the fish in the waters swim over my head
My love's gone and left me; he's the one I adore
I never will see him, no never, no more"
Chorus

She plunged her fair body in the water so deep
She closed her pretty blue eyes in the waters to sleep
And that lonesome maiden and her pitiful cries
Can be heard from the ocean to the heavenly skies
Chorus

I Know My Love

Key: D

I know my love by his way of wa-lk-ing I know my love by his way of ta-lk-ing I know my love dressed in his jer-sey blue, and if my love leaves me what will I do-o-o *and still she cried "I love him the best and a troub-led mind sure it knows no re-e-est" and still she cried "Bon-ny boys are few, and if my love leaves me what will I do".*

There is a dance house down in Mardyke
'Tis there my true love goes every night
He takes a strange girl upon his knee
And don't you think now that vexes me?
Chorus

If my love knew I could wash and wring
If my love knew I could weave and spin
I'd make a suit of the finest kind
But the want of money leaves me behind
Chorus

I know my love is an arrant rover
I know my love roams the wide world over
In some foreign town he may chance to tarry
And some foreign maid he will surely marry
Chorus

25

The Galway Shawl

(Verses and chorus have the same melody)

A shawl is a type of loose cloak worn by women throughout Ireland over the centuries.
Oranmore is a small rural town to the east of Galway city which lies at the head of Oranmore Bay, a creek of the larger Galway Bay, and is situated at the western extremity of the plain which covers central Ireland between Dublin and Galway city.
Donegal is the most north-westerly county in Ireland.

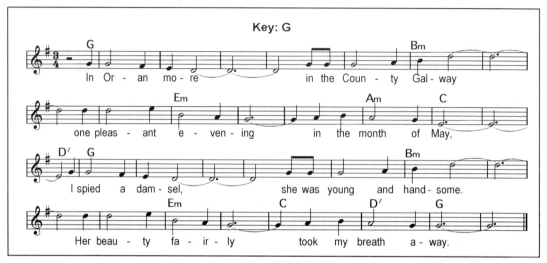

She wore no jewels, no costly diamonds
No paint or powder, no none at all
She wore a bonnet with a ribbon on it
And around her shoulders was a Galway shawl

As we kept on walking she kept on talking
Till her father's cottage came into view
She said "Come in sir, and meet my father
And for to please him play the Foggy Dew"
Chorus

I played 'The Blackbird' and 'The Stack of Barley'
'Rodney's Glory' and 'The Foggy Dew'
She sang each note like an Irish linnet
And the tears they flowed in her eyes of blue
Chorus

'Twas early, early, all in the morning
I hit the road for old Donegal
She said "Goodbye sir" and her eyes seemed brighter
And my heart remained with the Galway shawl
Chorus

The Banks Of Claudy

Key: G

| | | G' | F | C | G |
'Twas on a pleas - ant mo - rn - ing all i - n the month of May.

| | | G' | C | F | G |
Down by the Banks of Cl - au - dy I care-less-ly wound my way.

| | | G' | C | F | G |
I o - ver-heard a maid - en and she tear-ful-ly did com-plain,

| | | G' | F | C | G |
"It's on the Banks of Clau - dy where my da - rl - ing do re-main".

I boldly stepped up to her, I took her by surprise
I own she did not know me, I being dressed in disguise
"Where are you going my fair one, my joy and heart's delight
Where are you going to wander this cold and windy night?"

"It's on the way to Claudy's banks, if you will please to show
Take pity on a stranger, for there I want to go
It's seven long years or better since Johnny has left this shore
He's crossing the wide ocean, where the foaming billows roar"

"He's crossing the wide ocean for honour and for fame
His ship's been wrecked so I've been told down on the Spanish Main"
"It's on the Banks of Claudy fair maiden whereon you stand
Now don't you believe young Johnny, for he's a false young man"

Now when she heard this dreadful news she fell into despair
For the wringing of her tender hands and the tearing of her hair
"If Johnny he be drowned no man alive I'll take
Through lonesome glens and valleys I'll wander for his sake"

Now when he saw her loyalty no longer could he stand
He fell into her arms saying "Betsy I'm the man".
Saying "Betsy I'm the young man who caused you all the pain,
And since we've met on Claudy's banks we'll never part again"

Twenty-One Years

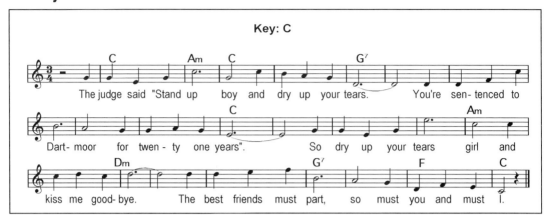

I hear the train coming, 'twill be here at nine
To take me to Dartmoor to serve out my time
I look down the railway and plainly I see
You standing there waiving your goodbyes to me

Six months have gone by, love, I wish I were dead
This cold dreary jail and a stone for my head
It's raining, it's hailing, the moon shows no light
Why won't you tell me, love, why you never write?

I've counted the days, love, I've counted the nights
I've counted the footsteps, I've counted the lights
I've counted the raindrops, I've counted the stars
I've counted a million of these prison bars

I've waited, I've trusted, I've longed for the day
A lifetime so lonely; my hair's turning grey
My thoughts are for you, love, till I'm out of my mind
For twenty-one years is a mighty long time

The Black Velvet Band

(Verses and chorus have the same melody)

This is a very popular Irish ballad about deportation, with a stern warning about never trusting the fairer sex! Many Irish men and women were deported, or 'transported' to Van Diemen's Land (originally referring to Tasmania, but over time it came to refer to Australia itself) by the British authorities during the 19th century, often for very petty crimes.
"Kilkenny" city is a large town in central Ireland, and is the principle town of County Kilkenny.

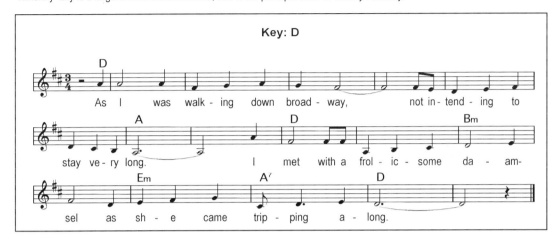

A gold watch she took out of her pocket and placed it right into my hand
On the very first time that I saw her; bad luck to the black velvet band

Her eyes they shone like diamonds; you'd think she was queen of the land
With her hair thrown over her shoulder; tied up with a black velvet band

'Twas in the town of Kilkenny; an apprentice to trade I was bound
With gaiety and bright amusement to see all the days go around
Till misfortune and trouble came over me which forced me to stray from the land
Far away from my friends and relations; betrayed by the black velvet band
Chorus

Before judge and jury next morning the both of us did appear
A gentleman swore to his jewellery and the case against us was clear
Seven long years' transportation away down to Van Diemen's Land
Far away from my friends and relations to follow the black velvet band
Chorus

Now all you brave young Irish lads a warning please gather from me
Beware of the pretty young damsels you meet all around Kilkenny
They'll treat you with whiskey and porter until you're unable to stand
And before you have time for to leave them you'll be sent down to Van Diemen's Land
Chorus

The Golden Jubilee

(Verses and chorus have the same melody)

Tralee is the chief town of County Kerry and the gateway to the Dingle Peninsula, situated in the south-west of Ireland. There's another ballad in this book about a girl from Tralee. See 'The Rose of Tralee' – page 6.

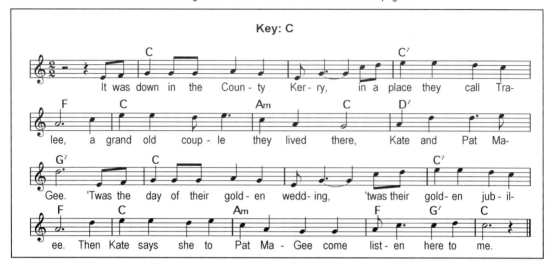

Put on your old knee britches and your coat of emerald green
Take off that hat me darling Pat, put on your old cáibin*
For today's our Golden Wedding and I'll have you all to know
Just how we looked when we were wed fifty years ago

Oh well do I remember how we danced on the village green
You held me in your arms dear Pat and called me your colleen
Your hair was like a raven's wing but now it's turning grey
Come over here my sweetheart dear and hear what I've to say
Chorus

Oh well do I remember when first I was your bride
In the little chapel on the hill where we stood side by side
Of good friends we've had plenty, of troubles we've had few
Come over here my sweetheart dear and here's what you must do
Chorus

*Pronounced "cawbeen" (cloth cap)

Maids When You're Young

(Verses and chorus have the same melody)

"Courting" is a quaint Irish verb which means, in its broadest sense, to "get romantically involved with". It would cover every activity from holding hands, to gentle kissing, to a whole lot of other things! I think that the girl in this ballad wants it to mean "a whole lot of other things!"

Key: G

An old man came court-ing me, hey ding dur-um da. An old man came court-ing me, me be-ing young. An old man came court-ing me, said he would mar-ry me. Maids when you're young nev-er wed an old man.

For he's got no folurum fol diddle-i-urum da
He's got no folurum fol diddle-i-aye
He's got no flurum, he's lost his ding-durum da
 Maids when you're young never wed an auld man

When we went to church, hey ding-durum da
When we went to church me being young
When we went to church he left me in the lurch
Maids when you're young never wed an auld man *Chorus*

When we went to bed, hey ding-durum da
When we went to bed me being young
When we went to bed he lay like he was dead
Maids when you're young never wed an auld man *Chorus*

I threw my leg over him hey ding-durum da
I threw my leg over him me being young
I threw my leg over him, damn nearly smothered him
Maids when you're young never wed an auld man *Chorus*

When he went to sleep, hey ding-durum da
When he went to sleep me being young
When he went to sleep out of bed I did creep
Into the arms of a willing young man
Chorus change:- "And I found his falurum, fol diddle-i-urum da", etc.

31

The Snowy-Breasted Pearl

The air of this ballad appears in "A General Collection of Ancient Irish Music" by Edward Bunting (1796), where it is attributed to Turlough O'Carolan. The lyrics are translated from Irish by George Petrie, who wrote "Ancient Music of Ireland" (1855). There is a great version of this ballad recorded by the Irish ballad group, The Wolfe Tones.

Oh thou blooming milk-white dove to whom I have aimed my love
Do not ever thus reprove my constancy
Now there are maidens would be mine with a wealth in land and kine
If my heart would but incline to turn from thee
But a kiss with welcome bland and a touch of thy fair hand
Are all that I demand, would'st thou not spurn
For if thou be not mine dear girl
Oh, thou snowy-breasted pearl
May I never from the fair with life return

The Cliffs Of Doneen

The Cliffs of Doneen are situated between the towns of Ballybunion and Ballylongford in County Kerry, on the estuary of the River Shannon on the west coast of Ireland. Although I have never been there myself, there are obviously fine views of West Clare from the Doneen Cliffs. Kilrush and Kilkee are two towns on the west coast of Clare.

My favourite version of this ballad is by the Irish folk and ballad singer, Christy Moore, on his album "Prosperous", recorded in 1971.

On the Western shores of County Clare is the wonderfully varied Atlantic coast, with mighty cliffs, caverns and sandy bays. To the north the rugged coast rises 700 feet above the sea at the sheer Cliffs of Moher. Extending for over five miles, these cliffs are home to puffins and guillemots, cormorants and rare fossils.

It's a nice place to be on a fine summer's day
Watching all the wild flowers that ne'er do decay
Oh the hares and the pheasants are plain to be seen
Making homes for their young 'round the Cliffs of Doneen

Take a view o'er the mountains, fine sights you'll see there
You'll see the high rocky mountains o'er the west coast of Clare
Oh the towns of Kilkee and Kilrush can be seen
From the high rocky slopes 'round the cliffs of Doneen

Fare thee well to Doneen, fare thee well for a while
And to all the kind people I'm leaving behind
To the streams and the meadows where late I have been
And the high rocky slopes 'round the Cliffs of Doneen

Fare thee well to Doneen, fare thee well for a while
And although we are parted by the raging sea wild
Once again I will wander with my Irish colleen
'Round the high rocky slopes of the Cliffs of Doneen

33

The Meeting Of The Waters

This ballad was written by Thomas Moore (1779 – 1852) who is renowned as one of Ireland's greatest songwriters. The tune is an ancient Irish air "The Old Head of Dennis".

Moore was a student in Trinity College, Dublin and was also a friend of Robert Emmet, the Irish patriot who led a small and abortive insurrection in Dublin in 1803 and was executed for his efforts. He was also acquainted with many of the United Irishmen and contributed to their newspaper, "The Press".

Combining his composition with famous Irish airs of the period, he published his works in the famous collections known as "Irish Melodies", but now more popularly known as "Moore's Irish Melodies" or "Moore's Melodies". There were ten volumes, the first appearing in 1807 and the final one (with a supplement) appearing in 1834. The "Irish Melodies" were immensely popular in Ireland and Britain.

Moore, in his "Irish Melodies" was seeking a rich and sophisticated audience for his Irish ballads and the first volume was dedicated to "the Nobility and Gentry of Ireland". Moore was attempting to portray a more peaceful side to Irish Nationalism and his ballads are a far cry from the blood-thirsty and rebel-rousing ballads which proliferated the streets and ale houses in the early nineteenth century.

There were two distinctly different attitudes among Irishmen towards Moore's ballads. Many though that he had achieved more to awaken the nationalistic spirit of Irishmen than the rebel-rousing ballads more familiar to the Irish ear, while others regarded them as whinging songs, bemoaning our downtrodden state and hanging from the coat-tails of the oppressor pleading for mercy. Some of Moore's ballads were reprinted on street ballad broadsheets throughout the middle years of the nineteenth century, particularly such songs as "Let Erin Remember", and the popular "The Minstrel Boy"

The ballads of Thomas Moore reproduced in this book do not reflect on the patriotic side of his writings, but more on the romantic - see "Believe Me, If All Those Endearing Young Charms" (page 20) and "The Last Rose of Summer" (page 12)

Written in 1807 this ballad is about a village and vale in County Wicklow (south of Dublin on the east coast) called Avoca, and the meeting of two rivers, the Avonmore and the Avonbeg. There are two meetings of these rivers in this vicinity – one at a place called Castle Howard and the other at Woodenbridge. Moore settled the question as to which of the scenes inspired his song in a letter to Lord John Russell in which he wrote "I believe the scene under Castle Howard was the one which suggested the song to me". Below the Meeting Bridge is the stump of a tree known locally as 'Moore's tree' against which Moore is said to have often rested, contemplating the scene before him.

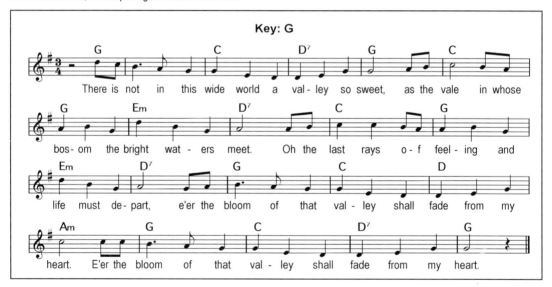

Yet it was not that Nature had shed o'er the scene
Her purest of crystal and brightest of green
'Twas not her soft magic of streamlet or hill
Oh no! It was something more exquisite still
Oh no! It was something more exquisite still

'Twas that friends, the belov'd of my bosom were near
Who made every dear scene of enchantment more dear
And who felt how the best charms of Nature improve
When we see them reflected from looks that we love
When we see them reflected from looks that we love

Sweet vale of Avoca how calm could I rest
In thy bosom of shade with the friends I love best
Where the storms that we feel in this cold world should cease
And our hearts like thy waters be mingled in peace
And our hearts like thy waters be mingled in peace

The Gypsy

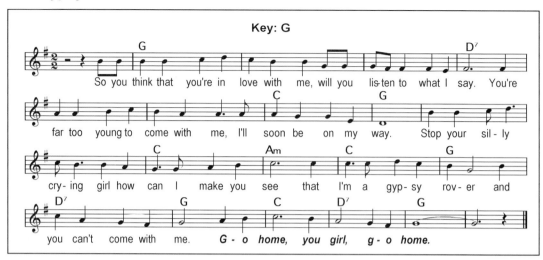

You met me at the marketplace when your Ma was not with you
You liked my long brown ringlets and my handkerchief of blue
Although I'm very fond of you and you asked me home to tea
I am a gypsy rover and you can't come with me
Chorus

Your brother is a peeler and he would put me in jail
If he knew I was a poacher and I hunt your lord's best game
Your daddy is a gentleman, your mammy's just as grand
But I'm a gypsy rover; I'll not be your husband
Chorus

The hour is drawing on my love and your ma's expecting thee
Don't you say you met me here for I'm just a gypsy
Please let go my jacket now; your love will have to wait
For I am twenty-two years old and you are only eight
Chorus

The Rose Of Allendale

Where e'er I wandered, east or west; though fate began to lour
A solace still she was to me in sorrow's lonely hour
When tempests lashed our lonesome barque and tore her shiv'ring sail
One maiden form withstood the storm; 'twas the Rose of Allendale
Chorus

And when my fevered lips were parched on Africa's hot sands
She whispered hopes of happiness and tales of distant lands
My life has been a wilderness, unblessed by fortune's gale
Had fate not linked my lot to hers, the Rose of Allendale
Chorus

The Boys From The County Armagh

The County of Armagh is situated in the north east of Ireland. It is the smallest of the six counties of Northern Ireland. This is a very popular song all over Ireland due to some extent to its very catchy chorus. Naturally, it's a great favourite in County Armagh itself!

The town of Armagh is the ecclesiastical capital of Ireland, the seat both of the Cardinal Archbishop and Catholic Primate of All Ireland, and the Protestant Archbishop. Hence the reference to "cathedral city".

Brian Boru (d. 1014), High King of Ireland, visited Armagh in 1005 and was received with great pomp and ceremony. The precious Book of Armagh was placed in his hands and his visit was duly recorded in it. He presented 20 ounces of pure gold to the Armagh clergy before ending his visit. After the Battle of Clontarf (1014) in which Brian and his son were slain, the bodies were brought to St. Patrick's Cathedral in Armagh and were buried there. The period of mourning for the dead lasted twelve days and on the day of the burial the Book of Armagh was borne before the King's coffin.

The sacred Book of Armagh, one of Ireland's most precious heirlooms, can be seen in the Library of Trinity College, Dublin. The book is a copy of the New Testament made for Abbot Torbach (d. 808) of Armagh in 807 by the master-scribe Ferdomnach (d. 846). This book is the subject of special interest for historians because it contains at the front a collection of 7th century texts about Saint Patrick and at the back a copy of the 4th century Life of Saint Martin of Tours.

Newtown, Forkhill, Crossmaglen and Blackwater are well known placenames and towns in County Armagh.

I've travelled that part of the county; Through Newtown, Forkhill, Crossmaglen
Around by the gap of Mount Norris; And home by Blackwater again
Where girls are so fair and so pretty; None better you'll find near or far
But where are the boys that can court them; Like the boys from the County Armagh!
Chorus

~~~~~~~~~~~~~~

I Once Loved A Lass

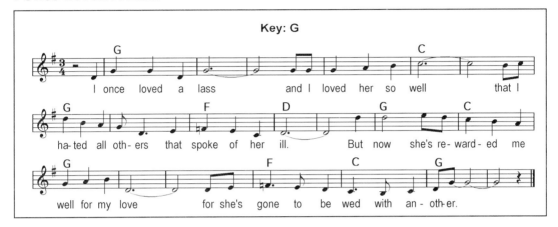

When I saw my love walk through the church door
With groom and bride maidens they made a fine show
And I followed them in with my heart full of woe
For now she is wed to another

When I saw my love a-sit down to dine
I sat down beside her and poured out the wine
I drank to the lassie that should have been mine
But now she is wed to another

The men in yon forest, they ask it of me
How many strawberries grow in the salt sea?
And I ask of them back with a tear in my eye
How many ships sail in the forest?

So dig me a grave and dig it so deep
And cover me over with flowers so sweet
And I will turn in for to take a long sleep
And maybe in time I'll forget her

They dug him a grave and they dug it so deep
They covered him over with flowers so sweet
And he has turned in for to take a long sleep
And maybe by now he's forgotten

Danny Boy

Undoubtedly one of the most popular ballads to be heard in the kitchens and pubs of Ireland! It is also one of the most consistently murdered ballads I know, because amateur balladeers normally start singing it too high and realise (when it is too late!) that they can't reach the high E note in the chorus. Keep that in mind – don't get caught out!

The melody of this ballad is called The Londonderry Air (or more simply, The Derry Air) and the ballad is often referred to by that name. However, as there are over 100 songs composed to that air it is more correct to call it 'Danny Boy'. (Thomas Moore composed a song to this air, called 'My Gentle Harp'.) The melody first appeared in print in the book, 'Ancient Music of Ireland' by the collector, George Petrie (1855).

The lyrics of Danny Boy were written by an English lawyer, Frederic Edward Weatherly (1848 – 1929). In 1910 he wrote the lyrics and music for an unsuccessful song he called Danny Boy. However in 1912 his sister-in-law sent him the melody of The Derry Air from America and he immediately noticed that his Danny Boy lyrics perfectly fitted the melody. In 1913 he published the song in its new form.

One of the most prolific and indefatiguable songwriters of his generation, Fred E. Weatherly published over fifteen hundred songs featuring music from a large number of composers. His most commercially successful ballad was 'Roses of Picardy' which became one of the most popular songs of the period of the First World War and which earned Weatherly a small fortune. Danny Boy was, and still is, a particular favourite in America where it was recorded by a number of popular singers, including Bing Crosby.

40

And when ye come and all the flowers are dying
And if I'm dead, as dead I well may be
You'll come and find the place where I am lying
And kneel and say an 'Avé' there for me
Chorus

And I shall hear, though soft you tread above me
And all my grave will warmer, sweeter be
If you will bend and tell me that you love me
Then I shall sleep in peace till you're with me
Chorus

As I Roved Out

My two favourite versions of this ballad are by the traditional group Planxty on their CD "Planxty" and also by The Woods Band on their album (I don't know if it's available on CD) "The Woods Band" (1971).

"And will you come to my mother's house when the moon is shining clearly (repeat)
I'll open the door and I'll let you in and divil the one will hear us". *Chorus*

So I went to her house in the middle of the night when the moon was shining clearly (repeat)
And she opened the door and she let me in and divil the one did hear us. *Chorus*

She took me horse by the bridle and the bit and she led him to the stable (repeat)
Saying "There's plenty of oats for a soldier's horse to eat them if he's able". *Chorus*

Then she took me by the lily-white hand and she led me to the table (repeat)
Saying "There's plenty of wine for the soldier boy to drink it if your able". *Chorus*

I got up and I made me bed and I made it nice and easy (repeat)
Then I took her up and I laid her down saying "Lassie are you able?" *Chorus*

And there we lay till the breaking of the day and divil the one did hear us (repeat)
Then I arose and put on me clothes, saying "Lassie, I must leave you". *Chorus*

"And when will you return again and when will we be married?" (repeat)
"When broken shells make Christmas bells, then will we be married". *Chorus*

Henry My Son

The earliest printed version of this ballad is in 1787 in "The Scots Musical Museum", under the title "Lord Ronald, My Son". This ballad is well known throughout Ireland, Britain and North America. The song is also known as "Lord Randall", "Jimmy Randal" and "Jimmy Randolph". It is thought that this ballad is associated with the death of Thomas Randolph (Randal), Earl of Moray, who died in 1332. Speculation has it that he may have been poisoned by his wife.

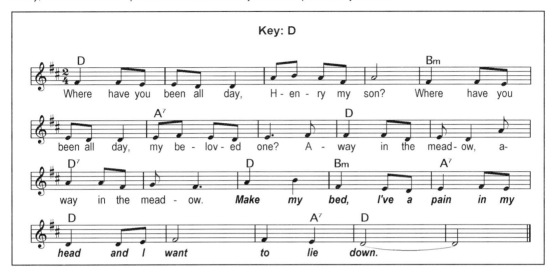

And what did you have to eat, Henry my son
What did you have to eat, my beloved one
Poisoned beads, poisoned beads
Chorus

What colour were those beads, Henry my son
What colour were those beads, my beloved one
Green and yellow, green and yellow
Chorus

What will you leave your mother, Henry my son
What will you leave your mother, my beloved one
A woollen blanket, a woollen blanket
Chorus

What will you leave your children, Henry my son
What will you leave your children, my beloved one
The keys of heaven, the keys of heaven
Chorus

And what will you leave your sweetheart, Henry my son
What will you leave your sweetheart, my beloved one
A rope to hang her, a rope to hang her
Chorus

The German Clockwinder

(Verses and chorus have the same melody)

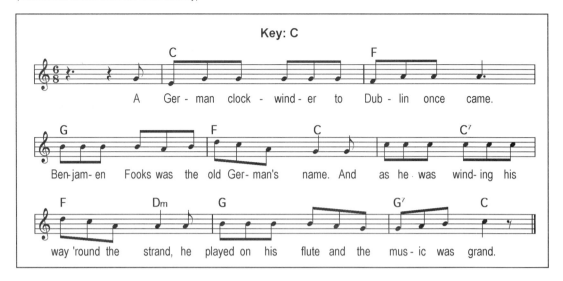

With me toor-a-lumma-lumma, toor-a-lumma-lumma, toor-a-lie-ay
Toor-a-lie, oor-a-lie, orr-a-lie-ay
Toor-a-lumma-lumma, toor-a-lumma-lumma, toor-a-lie-ay
Oor-a-lie, oor-a-lie, orr-a-lie-ay

Now there was a young lady from Grosvenor Square
Who said that her clock was in need of repair
In walks the bold German and to her delight
In less than five minutes he had her put right
Chorus

Now as they were seated down on the floor
There started a very loud knock on the door
In walked her husband and great was his shock
To see the bold German wind up his wife's clock
Chorus

The husband says he "Oh wife, Mary Ann
Don't let that bold German come in here again
He wound up your clock and left mine on the shelf
If your oul' clock needs winding I'll wind it myself!"
Chorus

The Nightingale

(Verses and chorus have the same melody)

This ballad is probably of English origin. The words and sentiments are very similar to several verses of a ballad which was printed in 1675 in London, entitled "The Nightingale's Song".
The romantic nightingale is a long distance migrant cousin of the familiar garden Robin. It is only active on these islands for a few weeks in late Spring. The most unique feature of this bird is, of course, that it sings at night-time and has therefore gained a reputation as a bird of romance. Its chirp, or voice, is very varied and noted for its contralto qualities with whistles and haunting repeated phrases.
We Irish would have quite an affiliation to the nightingale. You mightn't see us very much during the day, but at night-time we can be heard singing over long distances! There would be one subtle difference between ourselves and these beautiful birds, however – we tend to consume loads of beer in the course of this singing (indeed very often that is the reason for our singing in the first place). I don't think that the nightingale partakes of that activity!

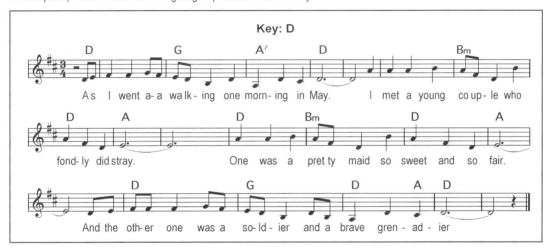

And they kissed so sweet and comforting as they clung to each other
They went arm-in-arm along the road like sister and brother
They went arm-in-arm along the road till they came to a stream
And they both sat down together for to hear the nightingale sing

From out of his knapsack he took a fine fiddle
And he played her such a merry tune with a hi-diddle-diddle
And he played her such a merry tune that the trees they did ring
And they both sat down together for to hear the nightingale sing. *Chorus*

Oh soldier, handsome soldier will you marry me
Oh no said the soldier that never can be
For I have a wife at home in my own country
And she is the sweetest little flower that you ever did see. *Chorus*

Now I am off to India for seven long years
Drinking wine and strong whiskey instead of cold beers
And if ever I return again it will be in the spring
And we'll both sit down together for to hear the nightingale sing. *Chorus*

45

The Lark In The Morning

The lark (or to use its official name 'Skylark', or *alauda arvensis*) is a very common bird in Ireland. It is estimated that over one million skylarks breed in Ireland each year. Their favourite habitats are the open country and coastal dunes. They make their nests on the ground, usually under clumps of tall grass. They often perch and sing on fence posts. One of the great characteristics of the skylark is their practice of flying at high altitude, especially over stubble fields where they find most of their food – cereal grain and insects.

It's one of the first birds to be heard in the morning in open countryside – hence they have acquired the reputation as a kind of symbol of the morning and the dawn of a new day. Its continuous song consists of a constant jumble of twittering, chirping and warbling sounds, often including the imitation of other song birds. It sings as it ascends into the heavens and hovers on fluttering wings, sometimes until it is almost out of sight.

If you want to keep your eyes open to spot skylarks their main features are sandy brown upper parts, streaked with dark brown. They have white outer tail feathers with a thin white trailing edge to their wings, visible only when open. Their underside consists of a white belly, buff breast with dark streaking heaviest on the sides. Their bills are pale, short and stubby. They have long legs, pale pink in colour with a very long claw on the hind toe. There is another song in this book relating to the skylark – see My Singing Bird (page 1).

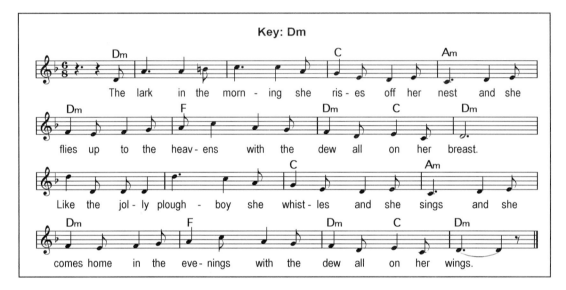

Oh Roger the ploughboy he is a dashing blade
He goes whistling and singing in yonder leafy shade
He met with dark-eyed Susan; she's handsome I declare
And she is far more enticing than the birds all in the air

As they were coming home from the rakes of the town
The meadow being all mown and the grass had been cut down
And as they should chance to tumble all in the new-mown hay
"Oh, it's kiss me now or never" this bonnie lass would say

When twenty long weeks were over and had passed
Her mammy asked the reason why she thickened 'round the waist
"It was the pretty ploughboy" this lassie then did say
"For he asked me for to tumble all in the new-mown hay"

Here's a health to you ploughboys wherever you may be
That like to have a bonnie lass a-sitting on each knee
With a pint of good strong porter he'll whistle and he'll sing
And the ploughboy is as happy as a prince or as a king

The Rose Of Mooncoin

(Verses and chorus have the same melody)

This is the county anthem of all the Kilkenny people around the world, written by Seamus Kavanagh who has written other Irish ballads, such as "Moonlight in Mayo" and "Biddy Mulligan". Kavanagh came from the village of Taghmon in County Wexford in the south-east of Ireland and had taken part in the Easter Rising of 1916 and the subsequent War of Independence.
Mooncoin is a small Kilkenny village situated beside the River Suir.
County Kilkenny, the ancient Kingdom of Ossory, has two river boundaries – the River Suir on the south-west and the River Barrow to the south-east. A third large river, the Nore, flows through the centre of the county in a pleasant wooded valley and joins the River Barrow near the point where it begins to widen into its long estuary. On the borders there's some high ground, notably the Slieveardagh and Booley Hills on the County Tipperary border and the hills around Graiguenemenegh near the River Barrow.
Centre of attraction in Kilkenny is, of course, Kilkenny City. It has the charm and atmosphere of an ancient settlement. Kilkenny is derived from the Irish 'Cill Chainnigh' – 'The Church of Canice'. Historians believe that this church existed in Kilkenny City from the sixth century and was founded by Saint Canice. The present Cathedral building dates from around 1285.

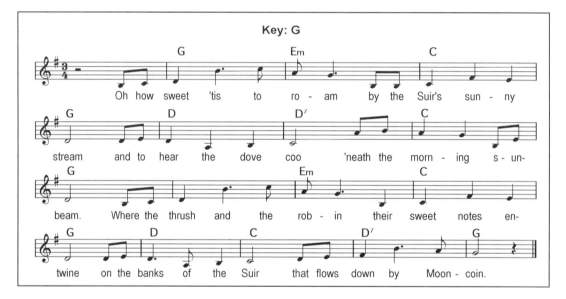

Flow on lovely river, flow gently along
By your waters so sweet sounds the lark's merry song
On your green banks I'll wander where first I did join
With you, lovely Molly, the Rose of Mooncoin

Oh Molly, dear Molly, it breaks my fond heart
To know that we shortly forever must part
I'll think of you Molly while sun and moon shine
On the banks of the Suir that flows down by Mooncoin
Chorus

She has sailed far away o'er the dark rolling foam
Far away from the hills of her dear Irish home
Where the fisherman sports with his small boat and line
By the banks of the Suir that flows down by Mooncoin
Chorus

Oh then here's to the Suir with its valleys so fair
Where oft times we wandered in the cool morning air
Where the roses are blooming and the lilies entwine
On the banks of the Suir that flows down by Mooncoin
Chorus

Nora

This song is also known as "Maggie" and was included by Sean O'Casey (with additional lyrics by himself) in his play "The Plough & the Stars". The original "Maggie" was written by the Canadian, George Johnson in 1863 to an air composed by James A. Butterfield.

The golden dewed daffodils shone, Nora
And danced in the breeze on the lea
When I first said I loved only you, Nora
And you said you loved only me
The birds in the trees sang their songs, Nora
Of happier transports to be
When I first said I loved only you, Nora
And you said you loved only me

Our hopes they have never come true, Nora
Our dreams they were never to be
Since I first said I loved only you, Nora
And you said you loved only me
The violets are withered and gone, Nora
I cry for the years as they flee
Since I first said I loved only you, Nora
And you said you loved only me

The Butcher Boy

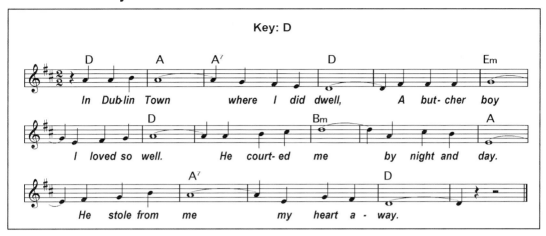

Key: D

In Dub-lin Town where I did dwell, A but-cher boy
I loved so well. He court-ed me by night and day.
He stole from me my heart a - way.

I wish my baby it was born, and smiling on its daddy's knee
And my poor body to be dead and gone, with the long green grass growing over me

I'll go upstairs and make my bed; "What's there to do?" my mother said
My mother she has followed me, and saying "what's to come of thee?"
Chorus

"Oh mother dear you little know, my pain and sorrow and my woe
Go get a chair and sit me down; with pen and ink I'll write it down"

Her father he came home that night, enquiring for his heart's delight
He went upstairs the door he broke, and found her hanging by a rope
Chorus

He took a knife and cut her down, and in her bosom these lines he found
"Oh what a foolish girl was I, to give my heart to a butcher boy"

"Go dig my grave both wide and deep; put a marble stone at my head and feet
And in the middle a turtle dove, so the world might know I died for love
Chorus

Carrickfergus

This is an old and well known ballad which has acquired renewed popularity through the recording of it by Irish singer Van Morrison.

It was originally known as "The Sick Young Lover". The song in its present form may have evolved from two separate songs, which would explain why some of the lyrics don't quite make sense. A broadsheet containing both English and Irish verses was published in Cork in or around 1830.

The town of Carrickfergus in County Antrim, stands on the shores of Belfast Lough, about 11 miles from Belfast, the capital of Northern Ireland. It is a picturesque port in an old world setting. The two most interesting features of the town are the Norman Castle (one of the most impressive in Ireland and in an excellent state of preservation) and the imposing Church.

My childhood days bring sad reflections of happy times spent long ago
My boyhood friends and my own relations have all passed on now like the melting snow
So I'll spend my days in endless roving; soft is the grass, my bed is free
Ah, to be back now in Carrickfergus, on that long road down to the sea

Now in Kilkenny, it is reported there are marble stones as black as ink
With gold and silver I would transport her but I'll sing no more now till I get a drink
I'm drunk today and I'm seldom sober, a handsome rover from town to town
Ah, but I'm sick now and my days are over, so come all ye young lads and lay me down

Home Boys Home

Well I left my love behind me and I sailed across the tide
I said that I'd be back again and take her for my bride
But many years have passed and gone and still I'm far away
I know she is my fond true-love and waiting for the day
Chorus

Now I've learned there's more to life than to wander and to roam
Happiness and peace of mind can best be found at home
For money can't buy happiness and money cannot bind
So I'm going back tomorrow to the girl I left behind
Chorus

The Good Ship Kangaroo

(Verses and chorus have the same melody)

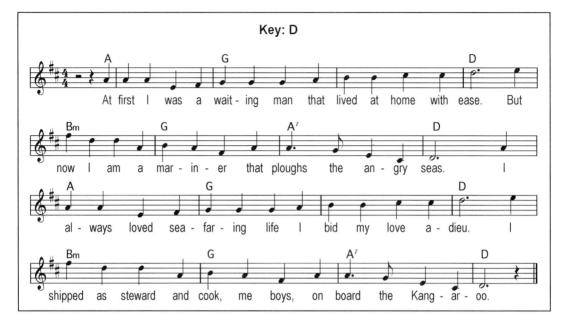

Oh I never thought she would prove false or either prove untrue
As I sailed away through Milford Bay on board the Kangaroo

"Oh think of me, oh think of me" she mournfully did say
"When you are in a foreign land and I am far away
Now take this lucky thrupenny bit, it'll make you bear in mind
The loving trusting faithful heart you left in tears behind

"Cheer up, cheer up my own dear love, don't weep so bitterly"
She sobbed, she sighed, she choked, she cried and could not say goodbye
"I won't be gone for very long, 'tis but a month or two
And when I do return again of course I'll marry you"
Chorus

Our vessel she was homeward bound from many's a far-off shore
And many's the foreign gifts and things unto my love I bore
I brought tortoises from Tenerife and toys from Timbuktu
A China rat, a Bengal cat and a Bombay cockatoo

Paid off, I sought her dwelling on the street above the town
Where a wiley dame upon the line was hanging out her gown
"Where is my love?". "She's married sir, about six months ago
To a smart young man who drives the van for Chaplin, Son and Co."
Chorus

My love she's not a foolish girl her age it is two score
My love she's not a spinster, she's been married twice before
I cannot say it was her wealth that stole my heart away
She was working in the laundry for one and nine a day.

Here's health to dreams of married life, to soap, to suds and blue
Heart's true love and patent starch and washing soda too
I'll go unto some distant shore no longer can I stay
And with some China Hottentot I throw myself away
Chorus

~~~~~~~~~~~~~~

The Kerry Dances

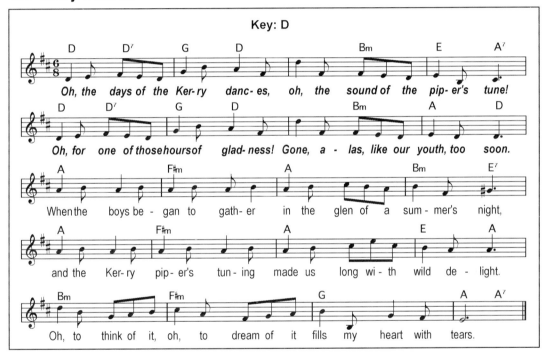

Chorus

*Was there ever a sweeter colleen in the dance than Eily More
Or a prouder lad than Thady as he boldly took the floor
"Lads and lassies to your places, up the middle and down again!"
And the merry hearted laughter ringing through the happy glen
Oh to think of it! Oh to dream of it!
Fills my heart with tears
Chorus

*First two lines sung to same melody as chorus

55

Sliabh Gallion Brae

This is a mournful song of exile and emigration centred in the area of Sliabh Gallion Brae. Sliabh Gallion Brae forms part of the Sperrin Mountains which occupy parts of Counties Derry and Tyrone in the Province of Ulster.

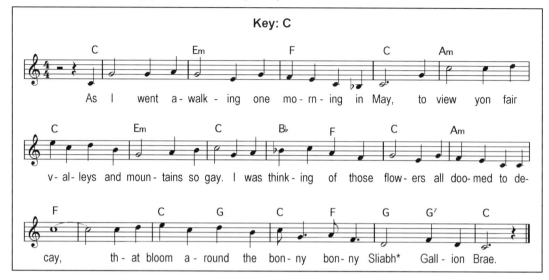

How oft in the morning with my dog and my gun
I roamed through the glens for joy and for fun
But those days are all over and I must go away
So farewell unto ye bonny bonny Sliabh Gallion Brae

How oft in the evening with the sun in the West
I roved hand in hand with the one I love the best
But the hopes of youth are vanished and now I'm far away
So farewell unto ye bonny bonny Sliabh Gallion Brae

It was not for the want of employment at home
That caused us poor exiles in sorrow to roam
But those tyrannising landlords they would not let us stay
So farewell unto ye bonny bonny Sliabh Gallion Brae

* Pronounced "shleeve" (mountain)

Also available
"130 Great Irish Ballads"
Containing every Irish ballad you can think of!
All the lyrics, guitar chords, simplified music score, plus a **CD** featuring the first verse and chorus of each song!

Available from our website:
http://www.music-ireland.ie

The full list of ballads on "130 Great Irish Ballads"

All For Me Grog
Arthur McBride
As I Roved Out
Avondale
Banks Of My Own Lovely Lee,
    The
Banks Of The Claudy, The
Banks Of The Roses, The
Banna Strand
Bard Of Armagh, The
Believe Me If All Those
    Endearing Young Charms
Black Velvet Band, The
Bold O'Donoghue
Bold Thady Quill
Bonny Boy, The
Boston Burglar, The
Botany Bay
Boulavogue
Boys Of Fairhill, The
Boys Of The County Armagh,
    The
Brennan On The Moor
Bunch Of Thyme, A
Bunclody
Butcher Boy, The
Carrickfergus
Cliffs Of Doneen, The
Cockles And Mussels
Come To The Bower
Courtin' In The Kitchen
Croppy Boy, The
Curragh Of Kildare, The
Danny Boy (The Derry Air)
Dicey Riley
Easy And Slow
Enniskillen Dragoon, The
Fiddlers Green
Finnegan's Wake
Foggy Dew, The
Follow Me Up To Carlow
Galway Races, The
Galway Shawl, The
German Clockwinder, The
Glendalough Saint, The

Golden Jubilee, The
Gypsy, The
Harp That Once Through Tara's
             Halls, The
Henry My Son
Highland Paddy
Hills Of Kerry, The
Holy Ground, The
Home By Bearna
I Know My Love
I Know Where I'm Going
I Never Will Marry
I Once Loved A Lass
I'll Tell Me Ma
I'm A Rover
James Connolly
Joe Hill
Johnny I hardly Knew Ye
Jolly Beggarman, The
Jug Of Punch, The
Juice Of The Barley, The
Kelly From Killane
Lanigan's Ball
Lark In The Morning, The
Last Rose Of Summer, The
Leaving Of Liverpool, The
Let Him Go, Let Him Tarry
Let The Grasses Grow
Look At The Coffin
Love Is Teasing
Maids When You're Young
Meeting Of The Waters, The
Mermaid, The
Merry Ploughboy, The
Minstrel Boy, The
Monto
Moonshiner, The
Mountains Of Mourne, The
Muirsheen Durkin
Mush Mush
My Singing Bird
Nation Once Again, A
Nightingale, The
Nora
O'Donnell Abú

Old Maid In The Garret
Old Woman From Wexford, The
Paddy Lay Back
Paddy's Green Shamrock Shore
Peggy Gordon
Quare Bungle Rye, The
Raggle Taggle Gypsy, The
Red Is The Rose
Reilly's Daughter
Rising Of The Moon, The
Rocks Of Bawn, The
Rocky Road To Dublin, The
Roddy McCorley
Rose Of Allendale, The
Rose Of Mooncoin, The
Rose Of Tralee, The
Rosin The Bow
Sally Gardens, The
Sam Hall
Scariff Martyrs, The
Sean South From Garryowen
She Moved Through The Fair
Shores Of Americay, The
Skibbereen
Slievenamon
Snowey Breasted Pearl, The
Spancil Hill
Spanish Lady, The
Star Of The County Down, The
Sweet Carnlough Bay
Three Lovely Lassies From
             Kimmage
Three Score And Ten
Tipping It Up To Nancy
Town Of Ballybay, The
Twenty-one years
Waxie's Dargle, The
Wearing Of The Green, The
Weile Waile
West's Awake, The
When You Were Sweet Sixteen
Whiskey In The Jar
Wild Colonial Boy, The
Wild Rover, The
Zoological Gardens, The

Removal of CD

Carefully cut along the perforated line to remove the CD from the CD case.
Your CD can be stored in this CD case, which is permanently fixed to this
book cover so that you can keep it safely with the book at all times.
Do not attempt to remove this CD case from the cover of the book as it will
result in damage to the book.